Nicolò Paganini

WERKE FÜR VIOLINE SOLO

Works for Solo Violin

Herausgegeben von | *Edited by*

Italo Vescovo

RICORDI

IMPRESSUM

Umschlagbild | *Cover picture*: Jean Auguste Dominique Ingres, *Niccolò Paganini*, New York, The Metropolitan Museum of Art

Deutsche Übersetzung von Birgit Gotzes
English translation by Avery Gosfield

Sy. 2999
ISMN 979-0-2042-2999-4

Inhalt | Contents

Einleitung

Die Kompositionen für Violine solo von Nicolò Paganini (1782–1840), das zeigt der neue *Catalogo tematico*[1], sind in seinem Œuvre nicht nur ein für sich stehendes Ganzes, sondern stellen zugleich einen zentralen Teil seines kompositorischen Werkes dar. Im Mittelpunkt stehen dabei die *Ventiquattro Capricci* op. 1, die 1820 bei Ricordi erschienen sind, doch außerdem gehören dazu Kompositionen, die sich in Stil und Struktur unterscheiden und die über einen sehr langen Zeitraum hin entstanden sind. Mit Ausnahme der *Ventiquattro Capricci,* die ganz zweifellos die wichtigsten, am besten erforschten und am häufigsten aufgeführten unter diesen Kompositionen sind, sowie einiger weiterer Stücke sind die restlichen Kompositionen für Violine solo des großen Geigers im Lauf der Zeit auf kein besonderes Interesse bei Musikwissenschaftlern und Interpreten gestoßen; diese haben dadurch allerdings eine Reihe musikalisch und stilistisch interessanter, origineller Werke vernachlässigt, die es verdienen, genauer analysiert zu werden. Zu ihnen gehören die in der vorliegenden Ausgabe enthaltenen Kompositionen, die über den langen Zeitraum zwischen 1796–1800 (Datum des *Tema variato* M.S. 82) und 1833 (Datum des *Caprice d'adieu* M.S. 68) entstanden sind.

Das *Tema variato*[2] für Violine solo (M.S. 82) ist ein frühes Werk, das zwischen 1796 und 1800 komponiert wurde, also in einer Zeit, in der auch Werke wie die *Carmagnola con variazioni* (M.S. 1) für Violine und Gitarre, das *Concerto in mi minore,* eine posthum veröffentlichte Komposition (M.S. 75), und der *Inno patriottico* für Violine (M.S. 81)[3] entstanden sind. Das *Tema variato,* ein Thema, dem sieben Variationen folgen, verweist bereits sehr explizit auf das für Paganini typische Konzept der Variation, für das die Auseinandersetzung mit instrumentaler Technik und Klang charakteristisch ist, wobei er ungewohnten Effekten wie dem „organetto", das durch Spielen nahe am Steg erzeugt wird, und dem „flagioletto" besondere Aufmerksamkeit gewidmet hat. Formal gesehen verkürzen die ungeraden Variationen das Thema (16 Takte unterteilt in zwei Perioden von acht Takten mit Ritornell), während alle geradzahligen 32 Takte zählen (mit Ausnahme der zweiten Variation, die nur 31 Takte hat), sie enden mit einem doppelten Taktstrich und der Spielanweisung „Volti subito". Es handelt sich insgesamt um eine Komposition aus regelmäßigen Phrasen und sich wiederholenden Symmetrien, die sowohl das Thema als auch die Variationen charakterisieren. In beiden erscheint die Wiederholung vollständiger Phrasen logisch und in Bezug auf die musikalische Konstruktion funktional. Das Manuskript des *Tema variato,* das nicht von Paganinis Hand stammt, liegt in Archivio Storico del Comune di Genova (Genua). Es besteht aus zwei Bögen (vier Seiten von 22 × 30 cm mit acht Notensystemen), die ineinander gelegt und jeweils beidseitig beschrieben sind.

Der *Valtz*[4] in A-Dur M.S. 80 ist eine kurze Komposition mit dreiteiliger Struktur (A-B mit einem *Da capo*-A), die seltsamerweise in das autographe Manuskript der *37 Sonate* für Gitarre M.S. 84 eingelegt ist. Das Werk entspricht im übrigen dem Part der ersten Violine aus dem *Valzer n. 2* der *Divertimenti carnevaleschi*[5]. Der *Catalogo tematico* bestätigt, dass es sich um eine eigenständige Komposition handelt: Darin werden Stücke erwähnt, die Paganini anlässlich gesellschaftlicher Ereignisse in Genua schrieb, darunter zum Beispiel die *Alessandrine* und *Valtz* für Violine solo[6]. Das Autograph von *Valtz* M.S. 80 liegt in der Biblioteca Casanatense in Rom.

1. Maria Rosa Moretti und Anna Sorrento. *Catalogo tematico delle musiche di Niccolò Paganini. Aggiornamento.* Hrsg. von Maria Rosa Moretti und Anna Sorrento. Einleitung und Anhang hrsg. von Maria Rosa Moretti. Mailand (Associazione Culturale Musica con le Ali) 2018. Auf diesen Katalog, abgekürzt CTA, bezieht sich die Signatur M.S.

2. Nicolò Paganini. *Tema variato.* M.S. 82. Kritische Ausgabe von Italo Vescovo. Mailand (Ricordi) 2019.

3. Die Manuskripte befinden sich heute im Archivio Storico del Comune di Genova (Genua).

4. Nicolò Paganini. *Valtz.* M.S. 80. Kritische Ausgabe von Italo Vescovo. Mailand (Ricordi) 2019.

5. Niccolò Paganini. *Divertimenti carnevaleschi* per due violini e basso M.S. 4. Kritische Ausgabe. Hrsg. von Italo Vescovo und Flavio Menardi Noguera. Mailand (Edizioni Suvini Zerboni) 2011.

6. Von Paganini komponierte Tänze für das Fest „Festone dei Giustiniani", das in einem Palazzo im historischen Zentrum von Genua stattfand. Dessen großer Salon wurde für öffentliche Bälle, Musikakademien, Karnevalsfeste und andere Veranstaltungen genutzt.

Die *Sonata a violino solo*[7] M.S. 6 ist eine ganz besonders faszinierende Komposition, genial nicht nur in technischer Hinsicht. Sie ist in Paganinis Zeit in Lucca (1805–1808?) entstanden und ist der Principessa Elisa Baciocchi gewidmet, einer Schwester Napoleons. Die *Sonata a violino solo* besteht aus zwei kurzen Sätzen (*Adagio – Allegro molto*) von insgesamt 46 Takten (16 + 30) und entfernt sich weit von der traditionellen Sonatenstruktur; der Begriff Sonate wird hier, wie auch in anderen Kompositionen Paganinis, einfach benutzt, um ganz generell ein formal freies Instrumentalwerk zu bezeichnen. Die Musik ist auf zwei Notensystemen geschrieben, um so auch graphisch zwei verschiedene Klangebenen anzuzeigen: Pizzicato im unteren System, mit dem Bogen im oberen. Das Autograph (ein Bogen von 22,5 × 30 cm mit 10 Notensystemen) liegt in der Biblioteca Casanatense in der sogenannten „Collezione postuma" von Kompositionen Nicolò Paganinis[8].

Das *Capriccio „In cor più non mi sento"*[9] M.S. 44 aus dem Jahr 1821 ist ein in der Originalversion des Komponisten fast unbekanntes Werk in zwei Sätzen, Andante und Presto, die jeweils aus dem Thema von Paisiello und einer virtuosen Variation (zur Unterscheidung von Bogenstrich und Pizzicato auf zwei Systemen notiert) bestehen. Bekannt ist hingegen die von Carl Guhr in seinem *Traktat* (S. 47–57) überlieferte Version, die den Titel *Introduction et Variations sur le Thème „Nel cor più non mi sento" pour le violon seul de Nicolo Paganini*[10] trägt. Diese letztere Version, deren Autograph unbekannt ist, ist umfangreicher und komplexer und wurde in den letzten zwei Jahrhunderten mehr oder weniger auf der Basis von Guhrs Edition mehrfach publiziert, insbesondere außerhalb von Italien. Dadurch geriet das *Capriccio* in Vergessenheit und wurde für eine Art von erstem Entwurf für ein umfangreicheres Werk gehalten. Die Originalität des Werkes, das als eigenständige Komposition betrachtet werden muss, wurde nicht erkannt. Das autographe Manuskript (20,5 × 14,5 cm) besteht aus zwei Blättern mit zehn Notensystemen und liegt in der Staatsbibliothek Berlin.

Das *Capriccio per violino solo* M.S. 54[11], das auf 1828 datiert und „S.E. il Signor Conte Maurizio Dietrichstein"[12] gewidmet ist, ist ein wirklich bemerkenswertes Werk, nicht nur wegen der Anordnung der Noten, die auf vier Systemen notiert sind, sondern auch wegen seiner musikalischen Konzeption, durch die es sich deutlich von den anderen *Capricci* unterscheidet. Die Technik der Polyphonie, die sich in vielen der Werke Paganinis für Violine solo zeigt und auf verschiedene Art ausgeführt ist, wird in dieser Komposition ins Extrem getrieben, jedenfalls auf der Ebene von Konzept und Notation. Die Struktur des kurzen Werkes (21 Takte in drei Phrasen von 4 und einer von 3 Takten, gefolgt von einer Coda mit 6 Takten) erinnert an die Partitur eines vierstimmigen Chorals. Gekennzeichnet ist das Werk durch einen kantablen, eleganten Stil, in dem die vier Stimmen polyphonisch geführt werden und so ein höchst raffiniertes harmonisches Gewebe entstehen lassen.

Das *Caprice d'adieu*[13] M.S. 68, dessen Autograph unbekannt ist, ist in einer gedruckten Ausgabe der *Six Caprices Caractéristiques pour le Violon op. 12* von Eduard Eliason[14] überliefert, die 1833 bei B. Schott erschienen ist; das *Capriccio* von Paganini findet sich im Anhang der Ausgabe. Es handelt sich um eine Komposition, deren Länge (48 Takte) und dreiteilige Struktur (||: A :||: B-A' :||) dem Modell von einigen der *Ventiquattro Capricci* op. 1 folgen. Doch im Vergleich mit diesen *Capricci*, die regelrechte Etüden sind, hat das *Caprice d'adieu* einen leichteren, scherzhaften Charakter. Technisch ist die Komposition weniger komplex, doch fehlt es ihr nicht an originellen musikalischen Ideen.

7. Nicolò Paganini. *Sonata a violino solo.* M.S. 6. Kritische Ausgabe von Italo Vescovo. Mailand (Ricordi) 2019.

8. Unter „Collezione postuma" (Nachgelassene Sammlung) ist die Gesamtheit der autographen oder nicht eigenhändigen Manuskripte aus dem Besitz von Paganini und seinen Erben zu verstehen, die auf diverse komplizierte Art mehrmals den Besitzer wechselten und schließlich 1972 vom italienischen Staat angekauft wurden und seither in der Biblioteca Casanatense in Rom liegen.

9. Nicolò Paganini. *Capriccio „In cor più non mi sento".* M.S. 44, Kritische Ausgabe von Italo Vescovo. Mailand (Ricordi) 2018.

10. Carl Guhr, *Ueber Paganinis Kunst die Violine zu spielen.* Mainz (B. Schott's Söhne) 1829 (Druckplatte 3194). In Italien erschien die Sammlung unter dem Titel *L'arte di suonare il violino di Nicolò Paganini* [...]. Mailand (Ricordi) 1834 (Druckplatte 7299). Im von Paganini selbst redigierten *Elenco de pezzi di musica da stamparsi* findet sich der Eintrag als Nr. 5: *Introduzione e Var.*[ni] *sul tema „Nel cor più".*

11. Nicolò Paganini. *Capriccio per violino solo.* M.S. 54. Kritische Ausgabe von Italo Vescovo. Mailand (Ricordi) 2019.

12. „[...] Ein sympathischer Mensch, geschickter Komponist [...], der dem Wiener Kulturleben eng verbunden war. Seine Großzügigkeit war sprichwörtlich, und sein Haus stand Dichtern und Musikern stets offen. Hier verkehrten Müller, Beethoven und Schubert, der ihm seinen *Erlkönig* widmete. [...] Dietrichstein unterstützte Paganini sehr bei der Organisation von Konzerten in Wien 1829." Philippe Borer. Foglio d'album. In: *Quaderni dell'Istituto di studi paganiniani.* VII/1993, S. 37.

13. Nicolò Paganini, *Caprice d'adieu.* M.S. 68. Kritische Ausgabe von Italo Vescovo. Mailand (Ricordi) 2017.

14. Über diesen Musiker ist so gut wie nichts bekannt. Auf der Seite 212 des *Catalogo tematico* (vgl. Anm. 1) findet sich der Hinweis: „Eduard Eliason, ein Freund von Paganini, war erster Geiger des London Philharmonic und Dirigent des Orchesters des Drury Lane Theaters in London."

Introduction

As can be seen in the revised *Catalogo tematico* (Thematic Catalogue),[1] Nicolò Paganini's works for solo violin, which constitute a *corpus* in themselves, are one of the most significant components of his musical production. These works, with the *Ventiquattro Capricci* op. 1 published by Ricordi in 1820 at their core, are made up of compositions that encompass a number of contrasting characters and structures that were written during different periods of Paganini's life. In essence, besides the 24 caprices, without a doubt the most important, the most studied and the most performed of this group, and a few other compositions, none of the other works for solo violin have generated particular interest on the part of scholars (or performers) of the works of the great violinist, to the detriment of a group of pieces that deserve greater consideration and study for their originality and distinctive character. Among these are found the compositions included in the present collection, which date from sometime between 1796 and 1800 (the date of the *Tema variato* M.S. 82) to 1833 (date of the *Caprice d'adieu* M.S. 68).

The *Tema variato*[2] for solo violin is a piece that belongs to the Genoese composer's juvenile period: according to the musicologist Edward Neill, it was composed between 1796 and 1800. Other works written during this period include *Carmagnola con variazioni* (M.S. 1) for violin and guitar, the posthumous "Grande Concerto" (E minor concerto M.S. 75) and *Inno patriottico* for violin (M.S. 81).[3] Paganini's *Tema variato*, a theme followed by seven variations, foreshadows his personal concept of variation in a clear manner, which is further illustrated by his exploration of sounds and instrumental techniques, with a focus on unusual effects such as "organetto", obtained by playing close to the bridge, and "flagioletto" (harmonics). As far as the form is concerned, the odd-numbered variations resemble the *Tema* (16 measures divided into sections of eight measures, each with a ritornello), while the even-numbered ones are 32 measures long—except for *Variazione II* which has 31—and end with a double barline without repeats, followed by the indication "Volti subito". In brief, we are dealing with a composition whose structure is made up of regular phrases and recurring symmetrical patterns that characterize both the *Tema* and its variations, where entire phrases are repeated in a way that seems logical and functions as part of the musical construction. The non-autograph manuscript of the *Tema variato*, held in the Historical Archives of the Municipality of Genoa (ms. 1793), is composed of two folios (four sheaves of paper, 22 × 30 cm in size, each one with eight music staves written on them) one inside of the other, all written on front and back.

The *Valtz* in A Major M.S. 80[4] is a short tripartite composition (A-B with *Da Capo*-A) that, curiously enough, was found tucked inside the autograph manuscript of the *37 Sonate* for guitar M.S. 84. In addition, the work is closely related to the first violin part of the *Valzer n. 2* from the *Divertimenti carnevaleschi*.[5] The TC confirms that it is a complete work in itself: as a matter of fact, it speaks of works written by Paganini for social occasions in Genova, among which the *Alessandrine* and *Valtz* for solo violino are mentioned.[6] The autograph manuscript of the *Valtz* M.S. 80 is held in the Biblioteca Casanatense in Rome.

The *Sonata a violino solo* M.S. 6[7] was composed during Paganini's years of service to the ducal court in Lucca (1805-1808) and dedicated to the sister of Napoleon, princess Elisa Baciocchi. Articulated in two short movements (Adagio – Allegro molto) for a total of 46 bars (16 + 30), the structure of the *Sonata a violino solo*

1. Maria Rosa Moretti and Anna Sorrento, *Catalogo tematico delle musiche di Niccolò Paganini*. Revised by Maria Rosa Moretti and Anna Sorrento. Introduction and Appendices by Maria Rosa Moretti, Milano, Associazione Culturale Musica con le Ali, 2018. All of the manuscript sigla used here are taken from this catalogue, henceforth referred to as TC.

2. Nicolò Paganini, *Tema variato* M.S. 82, crit. ed. Italo Vescovo (Milan: Ricordi, 2019).

3. The manuscripts are currently held in the Historical Archive in Genoa.

4. Nicolò Paganini, *Valtz* M.S. 80, crit. ed. Italo Vescovo (Milan: Ricordi, 2019).

5. Niccolò Paganini, *Divertimenti carnevaleschi per due violini e basso* M.S. 4, crit. ed. Italo Vescovo and Flavio Menardi Noguera (Milan: Edizioni Suvini Zerboni, 2011).

6. As with the *Divertimenti carnevaleschi*, these dances were composed by Paganini for the "Festone dei Giustiniani", held in a building in Genova's historical centre. Public balls, musical academies, carnivals and other forms of entertainment all took place in the great hall.

7. Nicolò Paganini, *Sonata a violino solo* M.S. 6, crit. ed. Italo Vescovo (Milan: Ricordi, 2016).

is not influenced by transalpine models: the term "sonata" generically indicates a freely elaborated instrumental piece. The piece is notated on double staves, *pizzicato* for the lower stave, and *arco* for the upper one, thereby visually reinforcing the aural effect created by two distinctly different planes of sound. The autograph manuscript of the *Sonata a violino solo* is housed in the Biblioteca Casanatense in Rome as part of the "Collezione postuma" of Nicolò Paganini's music.[8]

Composed in 1821 (according to the date in the original manuscript), the *Capriccio "In cor più non mi sento"* M.S. 44[9] is close to unknown in Paganini's own original, two movement version, which consists of an *Andante* with two variations on Paisello's theme, written on two staves (in order to separate the bowed notes from those played in *pizzicato*); followed by a brilliant, virtuosic *Presto*. In fact, the transcription found in Carl Guhr's treatise (pp. 47-57), known as *Introduction et Variations sur le Thème «Nel cor più non mi sento» pour le violon seul de Nicolo Paganini*,[10] is actually much more familiar. Although the original source of Guhr's version is unknown, it was in this form, far longer and more elaborate than that found Paganini's manuscript, that it would come to be known, and frequently published, (especially abroad), during the 19th and 20th centuries. Guhr's edition of the *Capriccio* eclipsed Paganini's, which came to be considered a kind of "first sketch" of a more extended work, thus ignoring its value and originality as a self-standing composition. The autograph manuscript (20,5 × 14,5 centimetres) is made up of two pages, each side containing 10 staves, and is housed in the Staatsbibliothek in Berlin.

The *Capriccio per violino solo* M.S. 54,[11] dated 1828, dedicated to "S.E. il Signor Conte Maurizio Dietrichstein",[12] is a truly unique work, not only for the way in which the music is organised (notated on four staves, one for each string) but also because of the way in which it was conceived musically, which clearly distinguishes it from the other *Capricci*. The concept of polyphony, which is, moreover, present and expressed in various ways in many of his violin works, is brought to an extreme level, at least in conceptual and visual terms, in this composition. Its brief structure (21 measures grouped into three phrases of four measures and one of three, followed by a six-bar coda) is reminiscent of a kind of four-part chorale written in score. It is characterised by its lyrical and elegant writing style, where the four voices move in polyphonic fashion, giving birth to an extremely refined harmonic texture.

In the absence of a surviving autograph manuscript, our primary source for the *Caprice d'adieu*[13] is a publication by Schott in 1833 of *Six caprices caractéristiques pour le violon* Op. 12 by Eduard Eliason,[14] in which Paganini's *Caprice* appears as an addendum. Consisting of 48 measures in rounded binary form (||: A :||: B-A' :||), the *Caprice d'adieu* shares a structural kinship with some of the *Capricci* Op. 1; but whereas the latter are full-blown etudes, this piece has a lighter, more whimsical character and presents less challenging technical demands. Nevertheless, while it may not reach the musical heights of the *Ventiquattro Capricci*, the *Caprice* contains original thematic material.

8. "Collezione postuma" refers to those musical documents, whether autograph or not, that belonged to Paganini and his heirs and subsequently changed ownership through various and complicated events until their acquisition by the Italian government in 1972 and final relocation to the Biblioteca Casanatense in Rome.

9. Nicolò Paganini, *Capriccio "In cor più non mi sento"* M.S. 44, crit. ed. Italo Vescovo (Milan: Ricordi, 2018).

10. Carl Guhr, *Ueber Paganinis Kunst die Violine zu spielen* (Mainz: B. Schott's Söhne, 1829). In Italy it was published with the name *L'arte di suonare il violino di Nicolò Paganini* [...] (Milan: Ricordi, 1834). In his *Elenco de pezzi di musica da stamparsi* (list of musical pieces to publish), edited by Paganini himself, *Introduzione e Var.ni sul tema "Nel cor più"* is at fifth place.

11. Nicolò Paganini, *Capriccio per violino solo* M.S. 54, crit. ed. Italo Vescovo (Milan: Ricordi, 2019).

12. "[...] A man with a likeable personality, an able composer [...] he had close ties to the Viennese cultural world. His generosity was legendary, and his house was always open to poets and musicians. Müller, Beethoven and Schubert were frequent visitors, with the latter dedicating his *Erlkönig* to him, [...] Dietrichstein aided Paganini a great deal in organising the concerts he held in Vienna in 1829". See: Philippe Borer, *Foglio d'album*, "Quaderni dell'Istituto di studi paganiniani", VII (1993), pp. 37-41: 37. Translation by Edward Neill.

13. Nicolò Paganini, *Caprice d'adieu* M.S. 68, crit. ed. Italo Vescovo (Milan: Ricordi, 2017).

14. We have very few biographical details regarding this musician. The Moretti and Sorrento *Catalogo tematico* reads: "Eduard Eliason, friend of Paganini, was first violin of the London Philharmonic and leader of the orchestra of the Drury Lane Theatre in London".

Tema variato

(M.S. 82)

4a corda
Var. II
Flagioletto
4a corda
Flagioletto
Volti subito

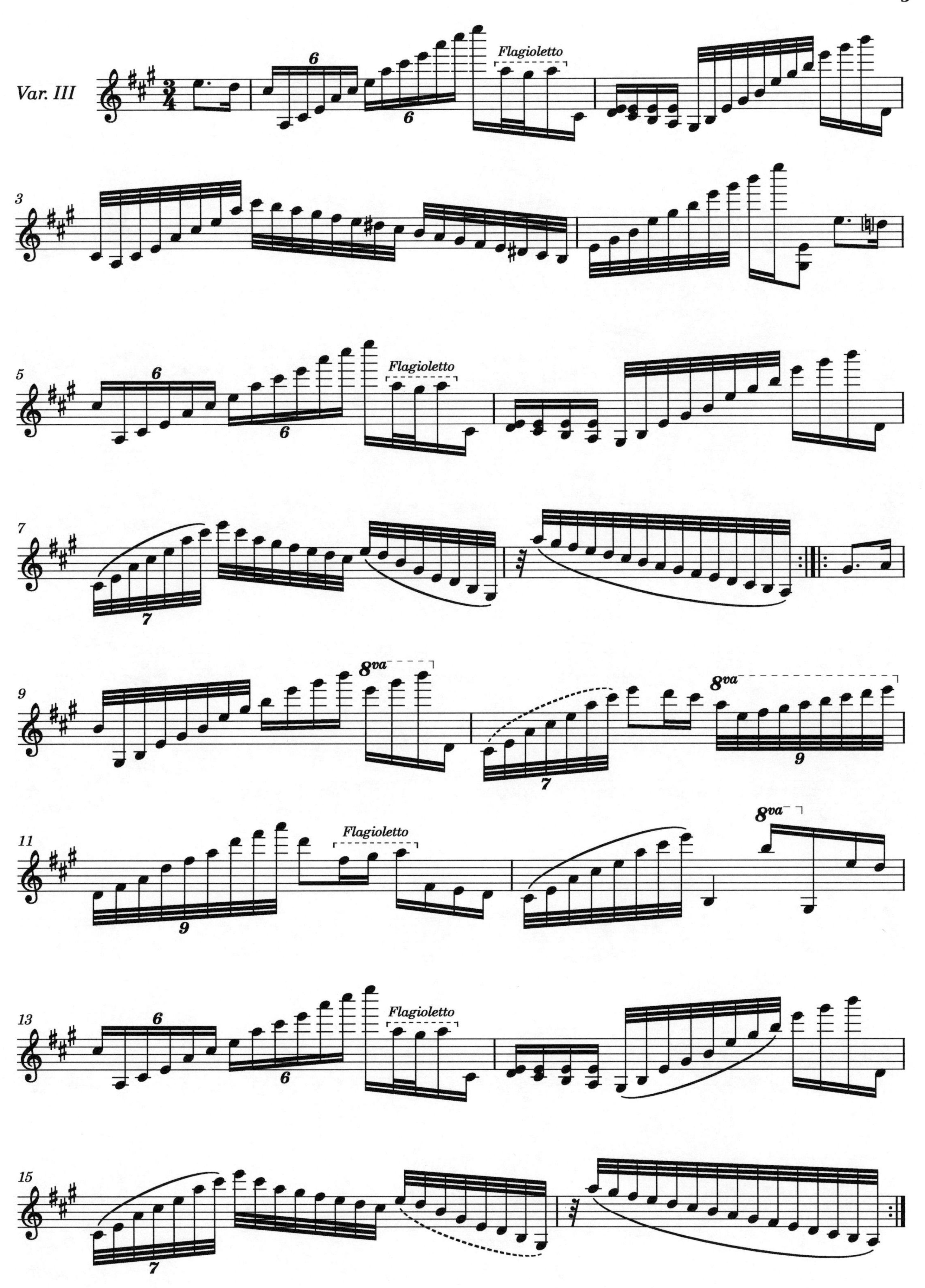
Var. III
6
6
Flagioletto
3
5
6
6
Flagioletto
7
7
9
8va
8va
7
9
11
Flagioletto
9
8va
13
6
6
Flagioletto
15
7

Organetto
Var. IV
Flagioletto
Organetto
Flagioletto
Volti subito

Var. V
[3]
6
6
6
8va
loco

4a corda
Var. VI
[3]
Flagioletto
4a corda
Flagioletto
Volti subito

Var. VII
8va
3
5
7
9
11
13
15
[8va]

Valtz

(M.S. 80)

Sonata a violino solo

(Merveille de Paganini)

(M.S. 6)

Allegro molto
dolce
6
11
16
21
26
cresc.
ff
Finis

Capriccio a violino solo

In cor più non mi sento

(M.S. 44)

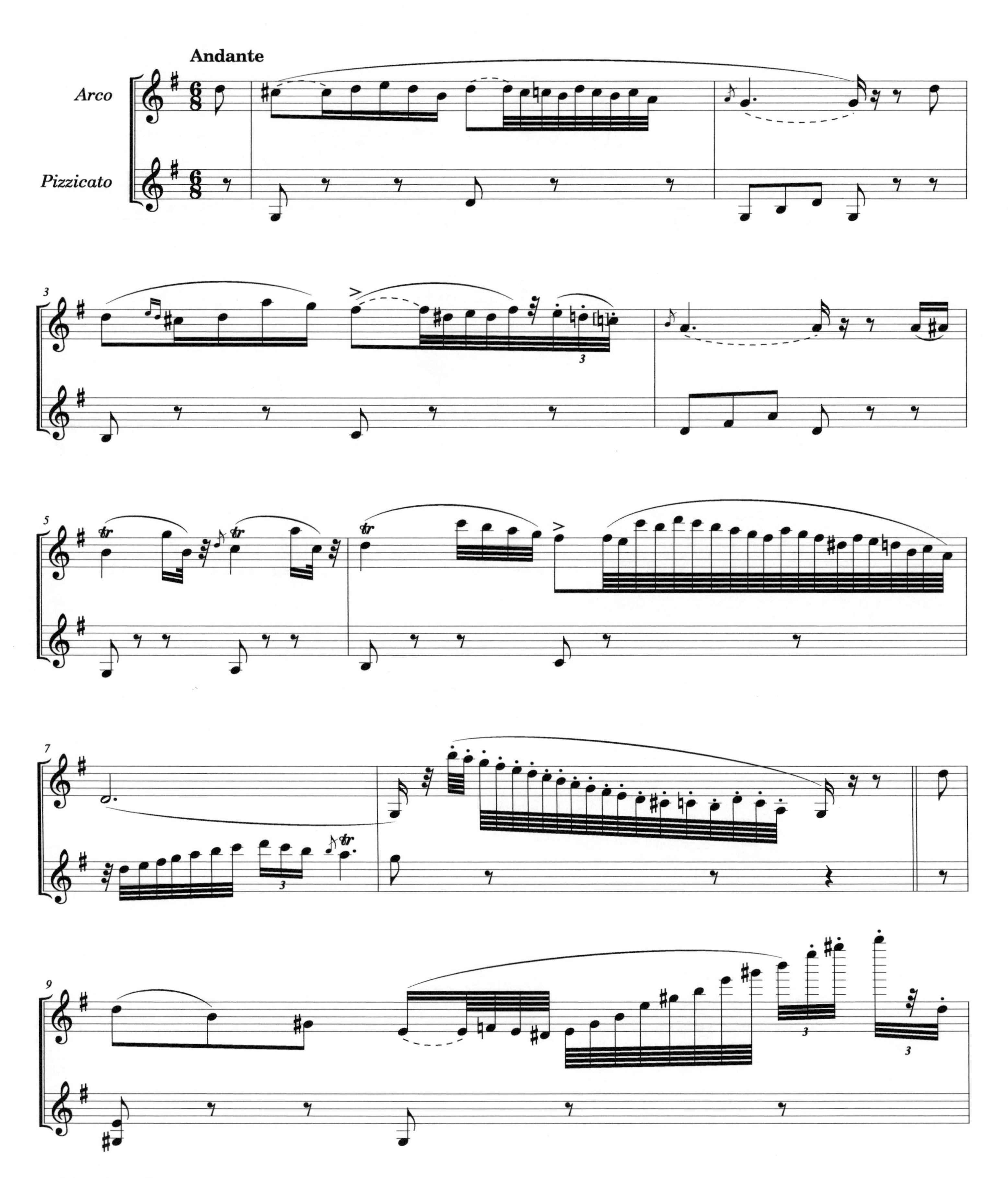

10
3.za corda
13
armonici
Forza
staccati
14
17
2a corda
19
trillo

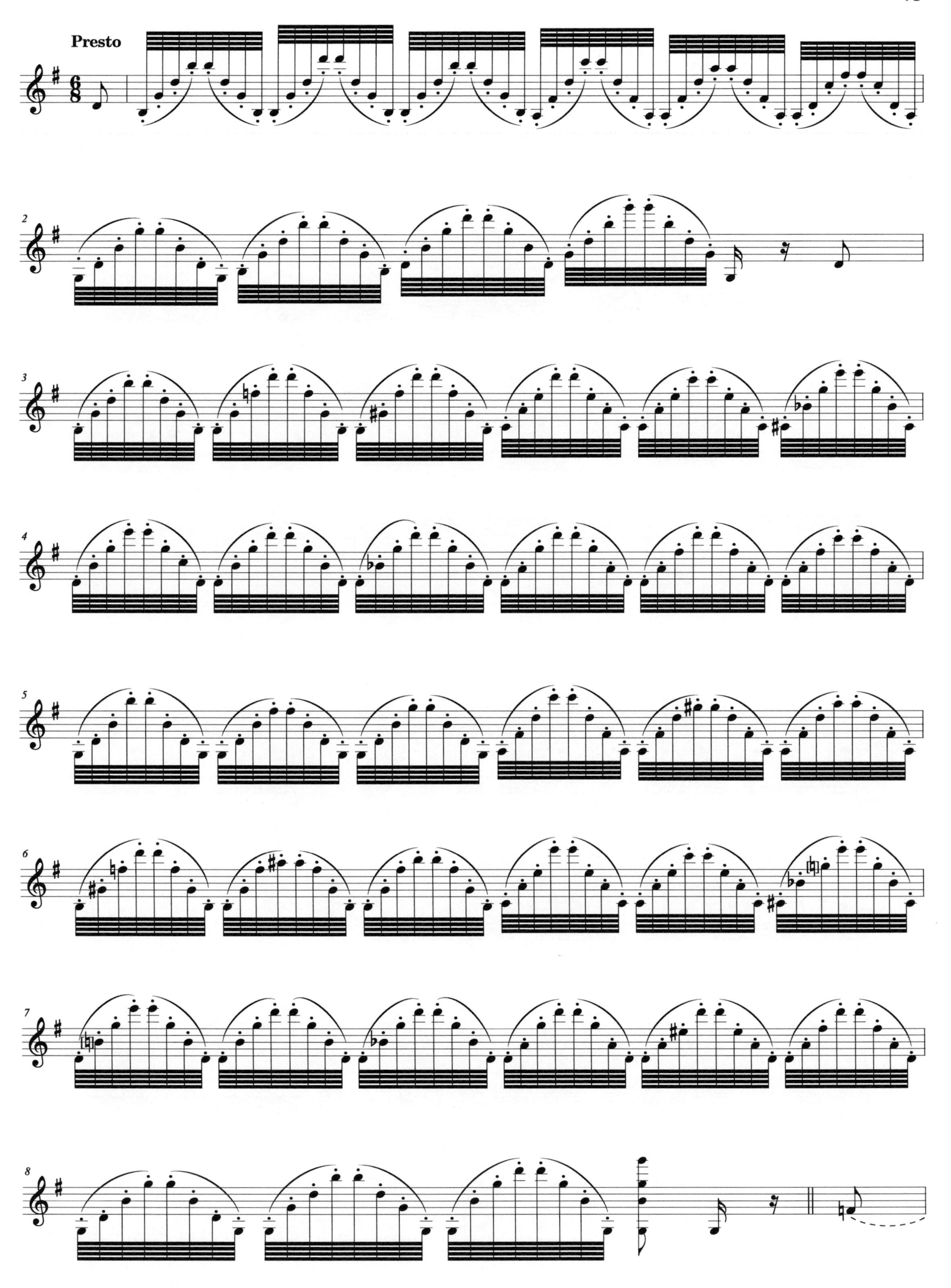
Presto

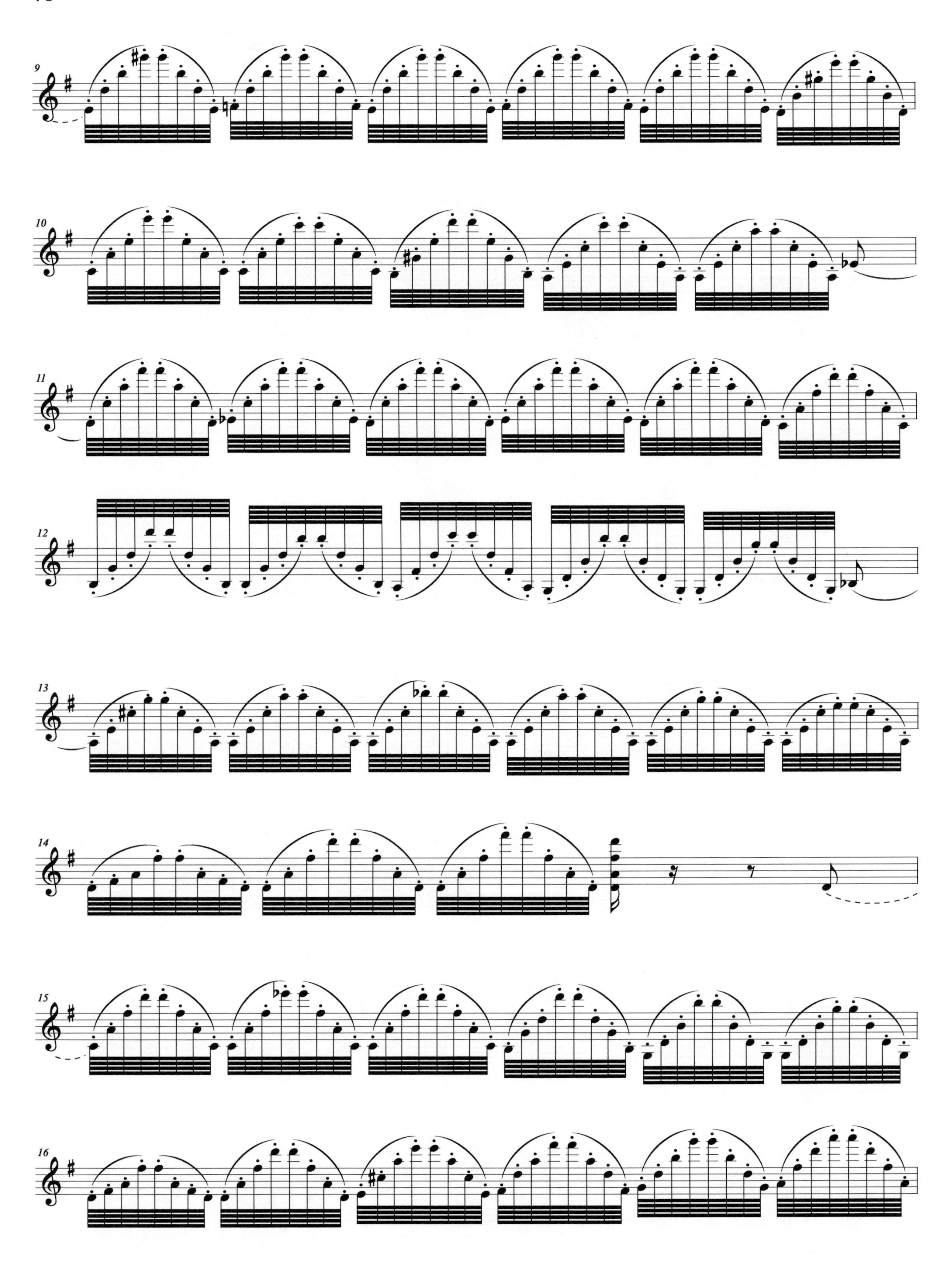
9
10
11
12
13
14
15
16

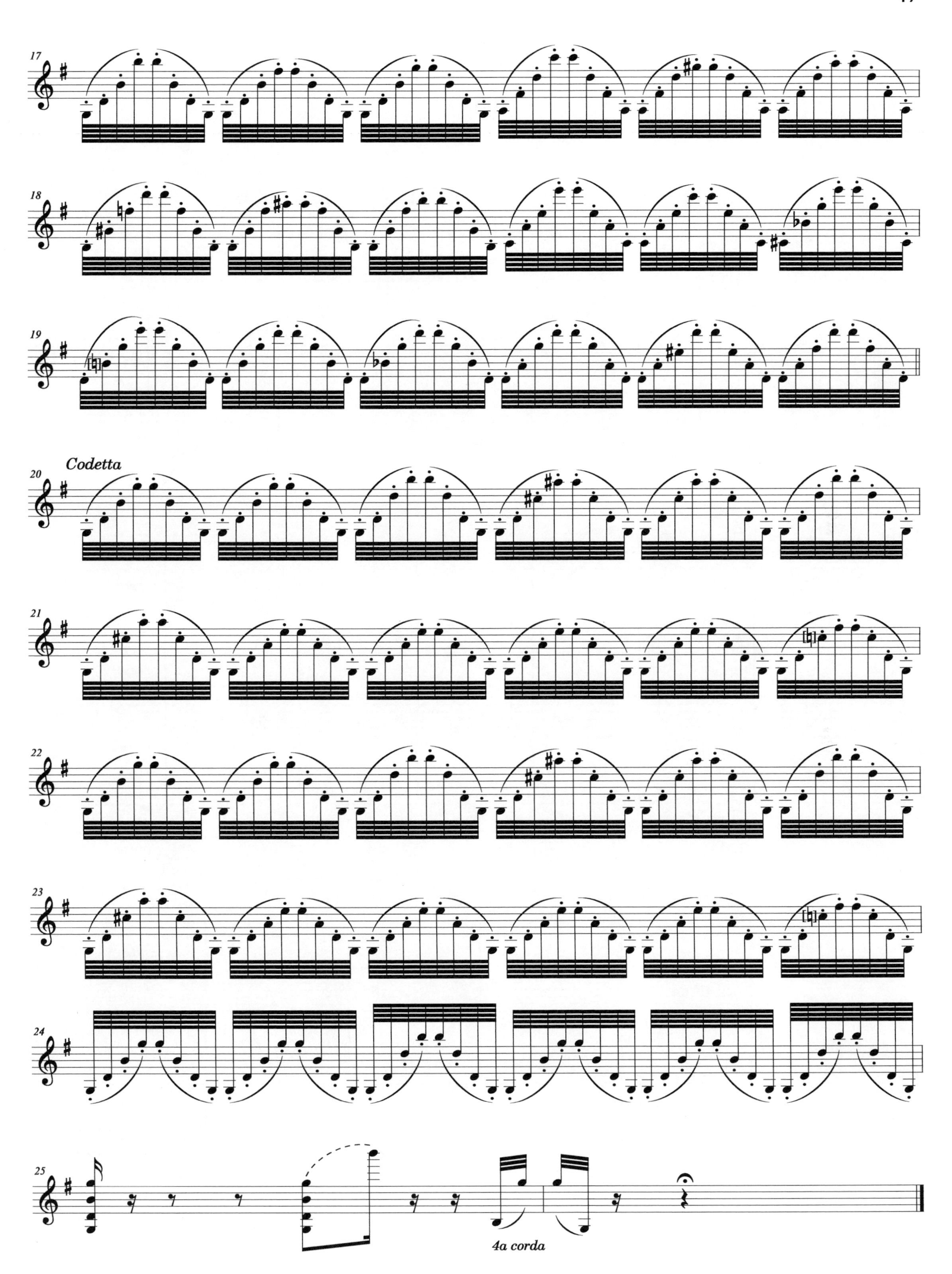

Codetta
4a corda

Capriccio per violino solo
(M.S. 54)

Vienna li 9. agosto 1828

Auf ein System übertragen von | *One-staff reduction by* Italo Vescovo

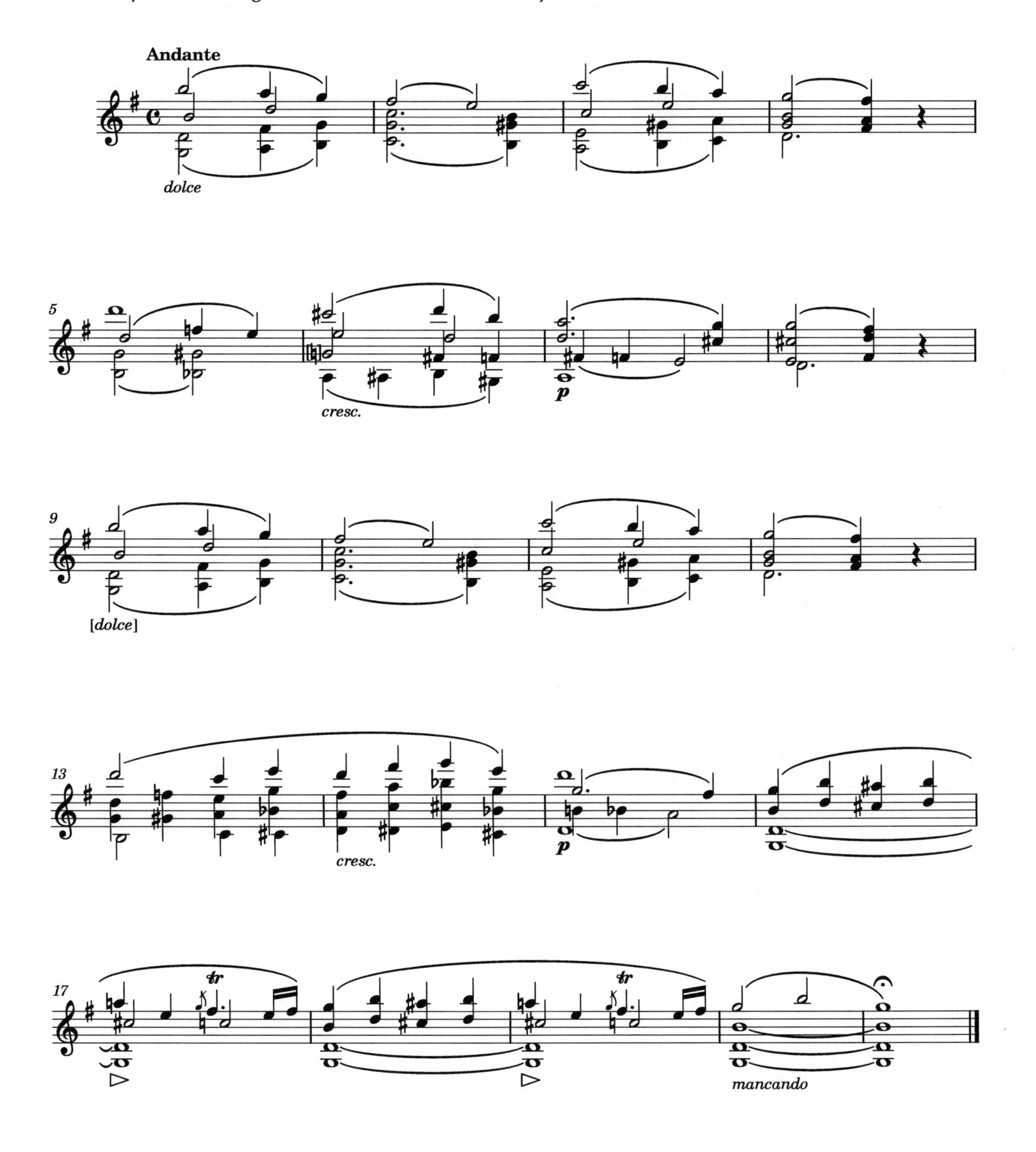

Caprice d'adieu

(M.S. 68)

Sy. 2999

dolce
cresc.
pizz.
Fine